MW00630467

# Camping

## The Camper's Journal

Nature is cheaper than therapy.

The "*Write It Down!*"® Series
by Journals Unlimited, Inc.

Printed in the USA using recycled materials.

Life is an adventure

It's not the destination we
reach that's most rewarding.
It's the journey along the way.

So **Write It Down!** & treasure
the memory forever. . .

Barbara Morina

Location:_____,_____ Date of Trip:_____

The weather / temperature was:_____

Campground name:_____

Phone number:_____,_____ Reservations needed by:_____

Site #:_____ Ideal Site #:_____ for possible return

Comments:_____

_____

The campground offered:_____

_____

Who I camped with:_____

_____

People I met:_____

_____

Places I visited:_____

_____

What I enjoyed most:_____

_____

Most memorable event:_____

_____

_____

Places to remember for the next time (restaurants, special attractions, entertainment, etc.):

_____

_____

_____

_____

_____

_____

_____

_____

_____

Notes:_____

_____

_____

_____

_____

_____

_____

_____

_____

_____

_____

_____

_____

_____

_____

_____

_____

_____

_____

_____

_____

_____

_____

_____

_____

_____

_____

_____

_____

_____

_____

Nothing left to say? Use this page to paste in your favorite photos!

Location:_____ Date of Trip:_____

The weather / temperature was:_____

Campground name:_____

Phone number:_____ Reservations needed by:_____

Site #:_____ Ideal Site #:_____ for possible return

Comments:_____

_____

The campground offered:_____

_____

Who I camped with:_____

_____

People I met:_____

_____

Places I visited:_____

_____

What I enjoyed most:_____

_____

Most memorable event:_____

_____

_____

Places to remember for the next time (restaurants, special attractions, entertainment, etc.):

_____

_____

_____

_____

_____

_____

_____

_____

_____

Notes:_____

_____

_____

_____

_____

_____

_____

_____

_____

_____

_____

_____

_____

_____

_____

_____

_____

_____

_____

_____

_____

_____

_____

_____

_____

_____

Nothing left to say? Use this page to paste in your favorite photos!

Location:_____ Date of Trip:_____

The weather / temperature was:_____

Campground name:_____

Phone number:_____ Reservations needed by:_____

Site #:_____ Ideal Site #:_____ for possible return

Comments:_____

_____

The campground offered:_____

_____

Who I camped with:_____

_____

People I met:_____

_____

Places I visited:_____

_____

What I enjoyed most:_____

_____

Most memorable event:_____

_____

_____

Places to remember for the next time (restaurants, special attractions, entertainment, etc.):

_____

_____

_____

_____

_____

_____

_____

_____

_____

Notes:_____

_____

_____

_____

_____

_____

_____

_____

_____

_____

_____

_____

_____

_____

_____

_____

_____

_____

_____

_____

_____

_____

_____

_____

_____

_____

_____

_____

_____

_____

_____

_____

*Nothing left to say? Use this page to paste in your favorite photos!*

Location:_____,_____ Date of Trip:_____

The weather / temperature was:_____

Campground name:_____

Phone number:_____ Reservations needed by:_____

Site #:_____ Ideal Site #:_____ for possible return

Comments:_____

_____

The campground offered:_____

_____

Who I camped with:_____

_____

People I met:_____

_____

Places I visited:_____

_____

What I enjoyed most:_____

_____

Most memorable event:_____

_____

_____

Places to remember for the next time (restaurants, special attractions, entertainment, etc.):

_____

_____

_____

_____

_____

_____

_____

_____

_____

Notes:

Nothing left to say? Use this page to paste in your favorite photos!

Location:_____ Date of Trip:_____

The weather / temperature was:_____

Campground name:_____

Phone number:_____ Reservations needed by:_____

Site #:_____ Ideal Site #:_____ for possible return

Comments:_____

_____

The campground offered:_____

_____

Who I camped with:_____

_____

People I met:_____

_____

Places I visited:_____

_____

What I enjoyed most:_____

_____

Most memorable event:_____

_____

_____

Places to remember for the next time (restaurants, special attractions, entertainment, etc.):

_____

_____

_____

_____

_____

_____

_____

_____

_____

Notes:_____

_____

_____

_____

_____

_____

_____

_____

_____

_____

_____

_____

_____

_____

_____

_____

_____

_____

_____

_____

_____

_____

_____

_____

_____

_____

_____

Nothing left to say? Use this page to paste in your favorite photos!

Location:_____,_____ Date of Trip:_____

The weather / temperature was:_____

Campground name:_____

Phone number:_____,_____ Reservations needed by:_____

Site #:_____ Ideal Site #:_____ for possible return

Comments:_____

_____

The campground offered:_____

_____

Who I camped with:_____

_____

People I met:_____

_____

Places I visited:_____

_____

What I enjoyed most:_____

_____

Most memorable event:_____

_____

_____

Places to remember for the next time (restaurants, special attractions, entertainment, etc.):

_____

_____

_____

_____

_____

_____

_____

_____

Notes:

Nothing left to say? Use this page to paste in your favorite photos!

Location:_____ Date of Trip:_____

The weather / temperature was:_____

Campground name:_____

Phone number:_____ Reservations needed by:_____

Site #:_____ Ideal Site #:_____ for possible return

Comments:_____

_____

The campground offered:_____

_____

Who I camped with:_____

_____

People I met:_____

_____

Places I visited:_____

_____

What I enjoyed most:_____

_____

Most memorable event:_____

_____

_____

Places to remember for the next time (restaurants, special attractions, entertainment, etc.):

_____

_____

_____

_____

_____

_____

_____

_____

_____

Notes:_____

_____

_____

_____

_____

_____

_____

_____

_____

_____

_____

_____

_____

_____

_____

_____

_____

_____

_____

_____

_____

_____

_____

_____

_____

_____

_____

_____

_____

Nothing left to say? Use this page to paste in your favorite photos!

Location:_____ Date of Trip:_____

The weather / temperature was:_____

Campground name:_____

Phone number:_____ Reservations needed by:_____

Site #:_____ Ideal Site #:_____ for possible return

Comments:_____

_____

The campground offered:_____

_____

Who I camped with:_____

_____

People I met:_____

_____

Places I visited:_____

_____

What I enjoyed most:_____

_____

Most memorable event:_____

_____

_____

Places to remember for the next time (restaurants, special attractions, entertainment, etc.):

_____

_____

_____

_____

_____

_____

_____

_____

Notes:

Nothing left to say? Use this page to paste in your favorite photos!

Location:_____ Date of Trip:_____

The weather / temperature was:_____

Campground name:_____

Phone number:_____ Reservations needed by:_____

Site #:_____ Ideal Site #:_____ for possible return

Comments:_____

_____

The campground offered:_____

_____

Who I camped with:_____

_____

People I met:_____

_____

Places I visited:_____

_____

What I enjoyed most:_____

_____

Most memorable event:_____

_____

_____

Places to remember for the next time (restaurants, special attractions, entertainment, etc.):

_____

_____

_____

_____

_____

_____

_____

_____

_____

Notes:

Nothing left to say? Use this page to paste in your favorite photos!

Location:_____ Date of Trip:_____

The weather / temperature was:_____

Campground name:_____

Phone number:_____ Reservations needed by:_____

Site #:_____ Ideal Site #:_____ for possible return

Comments:_____

_____

The campground offered:_____

_____

Who I camped with:_____

_____

People I met:_____

_____

Places I visited:_____

_____

What I enjoyed most:_____

_____

Most memorable event:_____

_____

_____

Places to remember for the next time (restaurants, special attractions, entertainment, etc.):

_____

_____

_____

_____

_____

_____

_____

_____

_____

Notes:

Nothing left to say? Use this page to paste in your favorite photos!

Location:_____ Date of Trip:_____

The weather / temperature was:_____

Campground name:_____

Phone number:_____ Reservations needed by:_____

Site #:_____ Ideal Site #:_____ for possible return

Comments:_____

_____

The campground offered:_____

_____

Who I camped with:_____

_____

People I met:_____

_____

Places I visited:_____

_____

What I enjoyed most:_____

_____

Most memorable event:_____

_____

_____

Places to remember for the next time (restaurants, special attractions, entertainment, etc.):

_____

_____

_____

_____

_____

_____

_____

_____

_____

_____

Notes:

Nothing left to say? Use this page to paste in your favorite photos!

Location:_____ Date of Trip:_____

The weather / temperature was:_____

Campground name:_____

Phone number:_____ Reservations needed by:_____

Site #:_____ Ideal Site #:_____ for possible return

Comments:_____

_____

The campground offered:_____

_____

Who I camped with:_____

_____

People I met:_____

_____

Places I visited:_____

_____

What I enjoyed most:_____

_____

Most memorable event:_____

_____

_____

Places to remember for the next time (restaurants, special attractions, entertainment, etc.):

_____

_____

_____

_____

_____

_____

_____

_____

Notes:

Nothing left to say? Use this page to paste in your favorite photos!

Location:_____._____ Date of Trip:_____

The weather / temperature was:_____

Campground name:_____

Phone number:_____._____ Reservations needed by:_____

Site #:_____ Ideal Site #:_____ for possible return

Comments:_____

_____

The campground offered:_____

_____

Who I camped with:_____

_____

People I met:_____

_____

Places I visited:_____

_____

What I enjoyed most:_____

_____

Most memorable event:_____

_____

_____

Places to remember for the next time (restaurants, special attractions, entertainment, etc.):

_____

_____

_____

_____

_____

_____

_____

_____

Notes:_____

_____

_____

_____

_____

_____

_____

_____

_____

_____

_____

_____

_____

_____

_____

_____

_____

_____

_____

_____

_____

_____

_____

_____

_____

_____

_____

_____

_____

_____

Nothing left to say? Use this page to paste in your favorite photos!

Location:_____,_____ Date of Trip:_____

The weather / temperature was:_____

Campground name:_____

Phone number:_____ Reservations needed by:_____

Site #:_____ Ideal Site #:_____ for possible return

Comments:_____

_____

The campground offered:_____

_____

Who I camped with:_____

_____

People I met:_____

_____

Places I visited:_____

_____

What I enjoyed most:_____

_____

Most memorable event:_____

_____

_____

Places to remember for the next time (restaurants, special attractions, entertainment, etc.):

_____

_____

_____

_____

_____

_____

_____

_____

Notes:

Nothing left to say? Use this page to paste in your favorite photos!

Location:_____,_____ Date of Trip:_____

The weather / temperature was:_____

Campground name:_____

Phone number:_____ Reservations needed by:_____

Site #:_____ Ideal Site #:_____ for possible return

Comments:_____

_____

The campground offered:_____

_____

Who I camped with:_____

_____

People I met:_____

_____

Places I visited:_____

_____

What I enjoyed most:_____

_____

Most memorable event:_____

_____

_____

Places to remember for the next time (restaurants, special attractions, entertainment, etc.):

_____

_____

_____

_____

_____

_____

_____

_____

_____

_____

Notes:

Nothing left to say? Use this page to paste in your favorite photos!

Location:_____ Date of Trip:_____

The weather / temperature was:_____

Campground name:_____

Phone number:_____ Reservations needed by:_____

Site #:_____ Ideal Site #:_____ for possible return

Comments:_____

_____

The campground offered:_____

_____

Who I camped with:_____

_____

People I met:_____

_____

Places I visited:_____

_____

What I enjoyed most:_____

_____

Most memorable event:_____

_____

_____

Places to remember for the next time (restaurants, special attractions, entertainment, etc.):

_____

_____

_____

_____

_____

_____

_____

_____

_____

Notes:

Nothing left to say? Use this page to paste in your favorite photos!

Location:_____,_____ Date of Trip:_____

The weather / temperature was:_____

Campground name:_____

Phone number:_____ Reservations needed by:_____

Site #:_____ Ideal Site #:_____ for possible return

Comments:_____

_____

The campground offered:_____

_____

Who I camped with:_____

_____

People I met:_____

_____

Places I visited:_____

_____

What I enjoyed most:_____

_____

Most memorable event:_____

_____

_____

Places to remember for the next time (restaurants, special attractions, entertainment, etc.):

_____

_____

_____

_____

_____

_____

_____

_____

_____

_____

Notes:

Nothing left to say? Use this page to paste in your favorite photos!

Location:_____ Date of Trip:_____

The weather / temperature was:_____

Campground name:_____

Phone number:_____ Reservations needed by:_____

Site #:_____ Ideal Site #:_____ for possible return

Comments:_____

_____

The campground offered:_____

_____

Who I camped with:_____

_____

People I met:_____

_____

Places I visited:_____

_____

What I enjoyed most:_____

_____

Most memorable event:_____

_____

Places to remember for the next time (restaurants, special attractions, entertainment, etc.):

_____

_____

_____

_____

_____

_____

_____

_____

Notes:_____

Nothing left to say? Use this page to paste in your favorite photos!

Location:_____,_____ Date of Trip:_____

The weather / temperature was:_____

Campground name:_____

Phone number:_____,_____ Reservations needed by:_____

Site #:_____ Ideal Site #:_____ for possible return

Comments:_____

_____

The campground offered:_____

_____

Who I camped with:_____

_____

People I met:_____

_____

Places I visited:_____

_____

What I enjoyed most:_____

_____

Most memorable event:_____

_____

_____

Places to remember for the next time (restaurants, special attractions, entertainment, etc.):

_____

_____

_____

_____

_____

_____

_____

_____

Notes:

Nothing left to say? Use this page to paste in your favorite photos!

Location:_____ Date of Trip:_____

The weather / temperature was:_____

Campground name:_____

Phone number:_____ Reservations needed by:_____

Site #:_____ Ideal Site #:_____ for possible return

Comments:_____

_____

The campground offered:_____

_____

Who I camped with:_____

_____

People I met:_____

_____

Places I visited:_____

_____

What I enjoyed most:_____

_____

Most memorable event:_____

_____

_____

Places to remember for the next time (restaurants, special attractions, entertainment, etc.):

_____

_____

_____

_____

_____

_____

_____

_____

_____

_____

Notes:

Nothing left to say? Use this page to paste in your favorite photos!

Location:_____ Date of Trip:_____

The weather / temperature was:_____

Campground name:_____

Phone number:_____ Reservations needed by:_____

Site #:_____ Ideal Site #:_____ for possible return

Comments:_____

_____

The campground offered:_____

_____

Who I camped with:_____

_____

People I met:_____

_____

Places I visited:_____

_____

What I enjoyed most:_____

_____

Most memorable event:_____

_____

_____

Places to remember for the next time (restaurants, special attractions, entertainment, etc.):

_____

_____

_____

_____

_____

_____

_____

_____

_____

Notes:

Nothing left to say? Use this page to paste in your favorite photos!

Location:_____,_____ Date of Trip:_____

The weather / temperature was:_____

Campground name:_____

Phone number:_____,_____ Reservations needed by:_____

Site #:_____ Ideal Site #:_____ for possible return

Comments:_____

_____

The campground offered:_____

_____

Who I camped with:_____

_____

People I met:_____

_____

Places I visited:_____

_____

What I enjoyed most:_____

_____

Most memorable event:_____

_____

_____

Places to remember for the next time (restaurants, special attractions, entertainment, etc.):

_____

_____

_____

_____

_____

_____

_____

_____

_____

Notes:

Nothing left to say? Use this page to paste in your favorite photos!

Location:_____,_____ Date of Trip:_____

The weather / temperature was:_____

Campground name:_____

Phone number:_____,_____ Reservations needed by:_____

Site #:_____ Ideal Site #:_____ for possible return

Comments:_____

_____

The campground offered:_____

_____

Who I camped with:_____

_____

People I met:_____

_____

Places I visited:_____

_____

What I enjoyed most:_____

_____

Most memorable event:_____

_____

_____

Places to remember for the next time (restaurants, special attractions, entertainment, etc.):

_____

_____

_____

_____

_____

_____

_____

_____

Notes:

Nothing left to say? Use this page to paste in your favorite photos!

Location:_____, Date of Trip:_____

The weather / temperature was:_____

Campground name:_____

Phone number:_____ Reservations needed by:_____

Site #:_____ Ideal Site #:_____ for possible return

Comments:_____

_____

The campground offered:_____

_____

Who I camped with:_____

_____

People I met:_____

_____

Places I visited:_____

_____

What I enjoyed most:_____

_____

Most memorable event:_____

_____

_____

Places to remember for the next time (restaurants, special attractions, entertainment, etc.):

_____

_____

_____

_____

_____

_____

_____

_____

_____

_____

Notes:

Nothing left to say? Use this page to paste in your favorite photos!

Location:_____, _____ Date of Trip:_____

The weather / temperature was:_____

Campground name:_____

Phone number:_____ Reservations needed by:_____

Site #:_____ Ideal Site #:_____ for possible return

Comments:_____

_____

The campground offered:_____

_____

Who I camped with:_____

_____

People I met:_____

_____

Places I visited:_____

_____

What I enjoyed most:_____

_____

Most memorable event:_____

_____

_____

Places to remember for the next time (restaurants, special attractions, entertainment, etc.):

_____

_____

_____

_____

_____

_____

_____

_____

_____

_____

Notes:_____

Nothing left to say? Use this page to paste in your favorite photos!

Location:_____,_____ Date of Trip:_____

The weather / temperature was:_____

Campground name:_____,_____

Phone number:_____,_____ Reservations needed by:_____

Site #:_____ Ideal Site #:_____ for possible return

Comments:_____

_____

The campground offered:_____

_____

Who I camped with:_____

_____

People I met:_____

_____

Places I visited:_____

_____

What I enjoyed most:_____

_____

Most memorable event:_____

_____

_____

Places to remember for the next time (restaurants, special attractions, entertainment, etc.):

_____

_____

_____

_____

_____

_____

_____

_____

_____

Notes:

Nothing left to say? Use this page to paste in your favorite photos!

Location:_____,_____ Date of Trip:_____

The weather / temperature was:_____

Campground name:_____

Phone number:_____,_____ Reservations needed by:_____

Site #:_____ Ideal Site #:_____ for possible return

Comments:_____

_____

The campground offered:_____

_____

Who I camped with:_____

_____

People I met:_____

_____

Places I visited:_____

_____

What I enjoyed most:_____

_____

Most memorable event:_____

_____

_____

Places to remember for the next time (restaurants, special attractions, entertainment, etc.):

_____

_____

_____

_____

_____

_____

_____

_____

Notes:

Nothing left to say? Use this page to paste in your favorite photos!

Location:_____ Date of Trip:_____

The weather / temperature was:_____

Campground name:_____

Phone number:_____ Reservations needed by:_____

Site #:_____ Ideal Site #:_____ for possible return

Comments:_____

_____

The campground offered:_____

_____

Who I camped with:_____

_____

People I met:_____

_____

Places I visited:_____

_____

What I enjoyed most:_____

_____

Most memorable event:_____

_____

_____

Places to remember for the next time (restaurants, special attractions, entertainment, etc.):

_____

_____

_____

_____

_____

_____

_____

_____

Notes:_____

_____

_____

_____

_____

_____

_____

_____

_____

_____

_____

_____

_____

_____

_____

_____

_____

_____

_____

_____

_____

_____

_____

_____

_____

_____

_____

_____

_____

_____

Nothing left to say? Use this page to paste in your favorite photos!

Location:_____,_____ Date of Trip:_____

The weather / temperature was:_____

Campground name:_____,_____

Phone number:_____,_____ Reservations needed by:_____

Site #:_____ Ideal Site #:_____ for possible return

Comments:_____

_____

The campground offered:_____

_____

Who I camped with:_____

_____

People I met:_____

_____

Places I visited:_____

_____

What I enjoyed most:_____

_____

Most memorable event:_____

_____

_____

Places to remember for the next time (restaurants, special attractions, entertainment, etc.):

_____

_____

_____

_____

_____

_____

_____

_____

_____

Notes:_____

_____

_____

_____

_____

_____

_____

_____

_____

_____

_____

_____

_____

_____

_____

_____

_____

_____

_____

_____

_____

_____

_____

_____

_____

_____

_____

_____

_____

_____

_____

Nothing left to say? Use this page to paste in your favorite photos!

Location:_____,_____ Date of Trip:_____

The weather / temperature was:_____

Campground name:_____

Phone number:_____ Reservations needed by:_____

Site #:_____ Ideal Site #:_____ for possible return

Comments:_____

_____

The campground offered:_____

_____

Who I camped with:_____

_____

People I met:_____

_____

Places I visited:_____

_____

What I enjoyed most:_____

_____

Most memorable event:_____

_____

_____

Places to remember for the next time (restaurants, special attractions, entertainment, etc.):

_____

_____

_____

_____

_____

_____

_____

_____

_____

Notes:

Nothing left to say? Use this page to paste in your favorite photos!

Location:_____,_____ Date of Trip:_____

The weather / temperature was:_____

Campground name:_____

Phone number:_____ Reservations needed by:_____

Site #:_____ Ideal Site #:_____ for possible return

Comments:_____

_____

The campground offered:_____

_____

Who I camped with:_____

_____

People I met:_____

_____

Places I visited:_____

_____

What I enjoyed most:_____

_____

Most memorable event:_____

_____

_____

Places to remember for the next time (restaurants, special attractions, entertainment, etc.):

_____

_____

_____

_____

_____

_____

_____

_____

_____

Notes:

Nothing left to say? Use this page to paste in your favorite photos!

Location:_____, _____ Date of Trip:_____

The weather / temperature was:_____

Campground name:_____

Phone number:_____ Reservations needed by:_____

Site #:_____ Ideal Site #:_____ for possible return

Comments:_____

_____

The campground offered:_____

_____

Who I camped with:_____

_____

People I met:_____

_____

Places I visited:_____

_____

What I enjoyed most:_____

_____

Most memorable event:_____

_____

_____

Places to remember for the next time (restaurants, special attractions, entertainment, etc.):

_____

_____

_____

_____

_____

_____

_____

_____

Notes:

Nothing left to say? Use this page to paste in your favorite photos!

Location:_____ Date of Trip:_____

The weather / temperature was:_____

Campground name:_____

Phone number:_____ Reservations needed by:_____

Site #:_____ Ideal Site #:_____ for possible return

Comments:_____

_____

The campground offered:_____

_____

Who I camped with:_____

_____

People I met:_____

_____

Places I visited:_____

_____

What I enjoyed most:_____

_____

Most memorable event:_____

_____

_____

Places to remember for the next time (restaurants, special attractions, entertainment, etc.):

_____

_____

_____

_____

_____

_____

_____

_____

Notes:

Nothing left to say? Use this page to paste in your favorite photos!

Location:_____,_____ Date of Trip:_____

The weather / temperature was:_____

Campground name:_____

Phone number:_____ Reservations needed by:_____

Site #:_____ Ideal Site #:_____ for possible return

Comments:_____

_____

The campground offered:_____

_____

Who I camped with:_____

_____

People I met:_____

_____

Places I visited:_____

_____

What I enjoyed most:_____

_____

Most memorable event:_____

_____

_____

Places to remember for the next time (restaurants, special attractions, entertainment, etc.):

_____

_____

_____

_____

_____

_____

_____

_____

_____

Notes:_____

_____

_____

_____

_____

_____

_____

_____

_____

_____

_____

_____

_____

_____

_____

_____

_____

_____

_____

_____

_____

_____

_____

_____

_____

_____

_____

_____

_____

_____

_____

_____

Nothing left to say? Use this page to paste in your favorite photos!

Location:_____ Date of Trip:_____

The weather / temperature was:_____

Campground name:_____

Phone number:_____ Reservations needed by:_____

Site #:_____ Ideal Site #:_____ for possible return

Comments:_____

_____

The campground offered:_____

_____

Who I camped with:_____

_____

People I met:_____

_____

Places I visited:_____

_____

What I enjoyed most:_____

_____

Most memorable event:_____

_____

_____

Places to remember for the next time (restaurants, special attractions, entertainment, etc.):

_____

_____

_____

_____

_____

_____

_____

_____

Notes:_____

_____

_____

_____

_____

_____

_____

_____

_____

_____

_____

_____

_____

_____

_____

_____

_____

_____

_____

_____

_____

_____

_____

_____

_____

_____

_____

_____

_____

_____

_____

_____

_____

Nothing left to say? Use this page to paste in your favorite photos!

www.journalsunlimited.com

Location:_____,_____ Date of Trip:_____

The weather / temperature was:_____

Campground name:_____

Phone number:_____ Reservations needed by:_____

Site #:_____ Ideal Site #:_____ for possible return

Comments:_____

_____

The campground offered:_____

_____

Who I camped with:_____

_____

People I met:_____

_____

Places I visited:_____

_____

What I enjoyed most:_____

_____

Most memorable event:_____

_____

_____

Places to remember for the next time (restaurants, special attractions, entertainment, etc.):

_____

_____

_____

_____

_____

_____

_____

_____

_____

Notes:

Nothing left to say? Use this page to paste in your favorite photos!

Location:_____,_____ Date of Trip:_____

The weather / temperature was:_____

Campground name:_____

Phone number:_____,_____ Reservations needed by:_____

Site #:_____ Ideal Site #:_____ for possible return

Comments:_____

_____

The campground offered:_____

_____

Who I camped with:_____

_____

People I met:_____

_____

Places I visited:_____

_____

What I enjoyed most:_____

_____

Most memorable event:_____

_____

_____

Places to remember for the next time (restaurants, special attractions, entertainment, etc.):

_____

_____

_____

_____

_____

_____

_____

_____

Notes:

Nothing left to say? Use this page to paste in your favorite photos!

Location:_____ Date of Trip:_____

The weather / temperature was:_____

Campground name:_____

Phone number:_____ Reservations needed by:_____

Site #:_____ Ideal Site #:_____ for possible return

Comments:_____

_____

The campground offered:_____

_____

Who I camped with:_____

_____

People I met:_____

_____

Places I visited:_____

_____

What I enjoyed most:_____

_____

Most memorable event:_____

_____

_____

Places to remember for the next time (restaurants, special attractions, entertainment, etc.):

_____

_____

_____

_____

_____

_____

_____

_____

_____

Notes:_____

_____

_____

_____

_____

_____

_____

_____

_____

_____

_____

_____

_____

_____

_____

_____

_____

_____

_____

_____

_____

_____

_____

_____

_____

_____

_____

_____

_____

Nothing left to say? Use this page to paste in your favorite photos!

Location:_____,_____ Date of Trip:_____

The weather / temperature was:_____

Campground name:_____,_____

Phone number:_____,_____ Reservations needed by:_____

Site #:_____ Ideal Site #:_____ for possible return

Comments:_____

_____

The campground offered:_____

_____

Who I camped with:_____

_____

People I met:_____

_____

Places I visited:_____

_____

What I enjoyed most:_____

_____

Most memorable event:_____

_____

_____

Places to remember for the next time (restaurants, special attractions, entertainment, etc.):

_____

_____

_____

_____

_____

_____

_____

_____

_____

Notes:_____

_____

_____

_____

_____

_____

_____

_____

_____

_____

_____

_____

_____

_____

_____

_____

_____

_____

_____

_____

_____

_____

_____

_____

_____

_____

_____

_____

_____

_____

_____

Nothing left to say? Use this page to paste in your favorite photos!

Location:_____ Date of Trip:_____

The weather / temperature was:_____

Campground name:_____

Phone number:_____ Reservations needed by:_____

Site #:_____ Ideal Site #:_____ for possible return

Comments:_____

_____

The campground offered:_____

_____

Who I camped with:_____

_____

People I met:_____

_____

Places I visited:_____

_____

What I enjoyed most:_____

_____

Most memorable event:_____

_____

_____

Places to remember for the next time (restaurants, special attractions, entertainment, etc.):

_____

_____

_____

_____

_____

_____

_____

_____

_____

Notes: _____

_____

_____

_____

_____

_____

_____

_____

_____

_____

_____

_____

_____

_____

_____

_____

_____

_____

_____

_____

_____

_____

_____

_____

_____

_____

_____

_____

_____

_____

_____

_____

_____

Nothing left to say? Use this page to paste in your favorite photos!

Location:_____,_____ Date of Trip:_____

The weather / temperature was:_____

Campground name:_____

Phone number:_____ Reservations needed by:_____

Site #:_____ Ideal Site #:_____ for possible return

Comments:_____

_____

The campground offered:_____

_____

Who I camped with:_____

_____

People I met:_____

_____

Places I visited:_____

_____

What I enjoyed most:_____

_____

Most memorable event:_____

_____

_____

Places to remember for the next time (restaurants, special attractions, entertainment, etc.):

_____

_____

_____

_____

_____

_____

_____

_____

_____

Notes:

Nothing left to say? Use this page to paste in your favorite photos!

Location:_____ Date of Trip:_____

The weather / temperature was:_____

Campground name:_____

Phone number:_____ Reservations needed by:_____

Site #:_____ Ideal Site #:_____ for possible return

Comments:_____

_____

The campground offered:_____

_____

Who I camped with:_____

_____

People I met:_____

_____

Places I visited:_____

_____

What I enjoyed most:_____

_____

Most memorable event:_____

_____

_____

Places to remember for the next time (restaurants, special attractions, entertainment, etc.):

_____

_____

_____

_____

_____

_____

_____

_____

_____

_____

Notes:

Nothing left to say? Use this page to paste in your favorite photos!

www.journalsunlimited.com

Location:_____ Date of Trip:_____

The weather / temperature was:_____

Campground name:_____

Phone number:_____ Reservations needed by:_____

Site #:_____ Ideal Site #:_____ for possible return

Comments:_____

_____

The campground offered:_____

_____

Who I camped with:_____

_____

People I met:_____

_____

Places I visited:_____

_____

What I enjoyed most:_____

_____

Most memorable event:_____

_____

_____

Places to remember for the next time (restaurants, special attractions, entertainment, etc.):

_____

_____

_____

_____

_____

_____

_____

_____

_____

_____

Notes:

Nothing left to say? Use this page to paste in your favorite photos!

Location:_____ Date of Trip:_____

The weather / temperature was:_____

Campground name:_____

Phone number:_____ Reservations needed by:_____

Site #:_____ Ideal Site #:_____ for possible return

Comments:_____

_____

The campground offered:_____

_____

Who I camped with:_____

_____

People I met:_____

_____

Places I visited:_____

_____

What I enjoyed most:_____

_____

Most memorable event:_____

_____

_____

Places to remember for the next time (restaurants, special attractions, entertainment, etc.):

_____

_____

_____

_____

_____

_____

_____

_____

Notes:

Nothing left to say? Use this page to paste in your favorite photos!

www.journalsunlimited.com

Location:_____ Date of Trip:_____

The weather / temperature was:_____

Campground name:_____

Phone number:_____ Reservations needed by:_____

Site #:_____ Ideal Site #:_____ for possible return

Comments:_____

_____

The campground offered:_____

_____

Who I camped with:_____

_____

People I met:_____

_____

Places I visited:_____

_____

What I enjoyed most:_____

_____

Most memorable event:_____

_____

_____

Places to remember for the next time (restaurants, special attractions, entertainment, etc.):

_____

_____

_____

_____

_____

_____

_____

_____

_____

Notes:

Nothing left to say? Use this page to paste in your favorite photos!

Location:_____,_____ Date of Trip:_____

The weather / temperature was:_____

Campground name:_____

Phone number:_____ Reservations needed by:_____

Site #:_____ Ideal Site #:_____ for possible return

Comments:_____

_____

The campground offered:_____

_____

Who I camped with:_____

_____

People I met:_____

_____

Places I visited:_____

_____

What I enjoyed most:_____

_____

Most memorable event:_____

_____

_____

Places to remember for the next time (restaurants, special attractions, entertainment, etc.):

_____

_____

_____

_____

_____

_____

_____

_____

_____

_____

Notes:

Nothing left to say? Use this page to paste in your favorite photos!

Location:_____,_____ Date of Trip:_____

The weather / temperature was:_____

Campground name:_____,_____

Phone number:_____,_____ Reservations needed by:_____

Site #:_____ Ideal Site #:_____ for possible return

Comments:_____

_____

The campground offered:_____

_____

Who I camped with:_____

_____

People I met:_____

_____

Places I visited:_____

_____

What I enjoyed most:_____

_____

Most memorable event:_____

_____

_____

Places to remember for the next time (restaurants, special attractions, entertainment, etc.):

_____

_____

_____

_____

_____

_____

_____

_____

_____

Notes:

Nothing left to say? Use this page to paste in your favorite photos!

Location:_____, _____ Date of Trip:_____

The weather / temperature was:_____

Campground name:_____

Phone number:_____,_____ Reservations needed by:_____

Site #:_____ Ideal Site #:_____ for possible return

Comments:_____

_____

The campground offered:_____

_____

Who I camped with:_____

_____

People I met:_____

_____

Places I visited:_____

_____

What I enjoyed most:_____

_____

Most memorable event:_____

_____

_____

Places to remember for the next time (restaurants, special attractions, entertainment, etc.):

_____

_____

_____

_____

_____

_____

_____

_____

_____

_____

Notes:

Nothing left to say? Use this page to paste in your favorite photos!

Location:_____, _____ Date of Trip:_____

The weather / temperature was:_____

Campground name:_____

Phone number:_____ Reservations needed by:_____

Site #:_____ Ideal Site #:_____ for possible return

Comments:_____

_____

The campground offered:_____

_____

Who I camped with:_____

_____

People I met:_____

_____

Places I visited:_____

_____

What I enjoyed most:_____

_____

Most memorable event:_____

_____

_____

Places to remember for the next time (restaurants, special attractions, entertainment, etc.):

_____

_____

_____

_____

_____

_____

_____

_____

_____

Notes:

Nothing left to say? Use this page to paste in your favorite photos!

Location:_____,_____ Date of Trip:_____

The weather / temperature was:_____

Campground name:_____

Phone number:____,_____ Reservations needed by:_____

Site #:_____ Ideal Site #:_____ for possible return

Comments:_____

_____

The campground offered:_____

_____

Who I camped with:_____

_____

People I met:_____

_____

Places I visited:_____

_____

What I enjoyed most:_____

_____

Most memorable event:_____

_____

_____

Places to remember for the next time (restaurants, special attractions, entertainment, etc.):

_____

_____

_____

_____

_____

_____

_____

_____

Notes:

Nothing left to say? Use this page to paste in your favorite photos!

Location:_____ Date of Trip:_____

The weather / temperature was:_____

Campground name:_____

Phone number:_____ Reservations needed by:_____

Site #:_____ Ideal Site #:_____ for possible return

Comments:_____

_____

The campground offered:_____

_____

Who I camped with:_____

_____

People I met:_____

_____

Places I visited:_____

_____

What I enjoyed most:_____

_____

Most memorable event:_____

_____

_____

Places to remember for the next time (restaurants, special attractions, entertainment, etc.):

_____

_____

_____

_____

_____

_____

_____

_____

_____

Notes:_____

_____

_____

_____

_____

_____

_____

_____

_____

_____

_____

_____

_____

_____

_____

_____

_____

_____

_____

_____

_____

_____

_____

_____

_____

_____

_____

_____

_____

_____

_____

_____

Nothing left to say? Use this page to paste in your favorite photos!

Location:_____,_____ Date of Trip:_____

The weather / temperature was:_____

Campground name:_____

Phone number:_____,_____ Reservations needed by:_____

Site #:_____ Ideal Site #:_____ for possible return

Comments:_____

_____

The campground offered:_____

_____

Who I camped with:_____

_____

People I met:_____

_____

Places I visited:_____

_____

What I enjoyed most:_____

_____

Most memorable event:_____

_____

_____

Places to remember for the next time (restaurants, special attractions, entertainment, etc.):

_____

_____

_____

_____

_____

_____

_____

_____

_____

Notes:

Nothing left to say? Use this page to paste in your favorite photos!

Location:_____ Date of Trip:_____

The weather / temperature was:_____

Campground name:_____

Phone number:_____ Reservations needed by:_____

Site #:_____ Ideal Site #:_____ for possible return

Comments:_____

_____

The campground offered:_____

_____

Who I camped with:_____

_____

People I met:_____

_____

Places I visited:_____

_____

What I enjoyed most:_____

_____

Most memorable event:_____

_____

_____

Places to remember for the next time (restaurants, special attractions, entertainment, etc.):

_____

_____

_____

_____

_____

_____

_____

_____

Notes:_____

Nothing left to say? Use this page to paste in your favorite photos!

Location:_____ Date of Trip:_____

The weather / temperature was:_____

Campground name:_____

Phone number:_____ Reservations needed by:_____

Site #:_____ Ideal Site #:_____ for possible return

Comments:_____

_____

The campground offered:_____

_____

Who I camped with:_____

_____

People I met:_____

_____

Places I visited:_____

_____

What I enjoyed most:_____

_____

Most memorable event:_____

_____

_____

Places to remember for the next time (restaurants, special attractions, entertainment, etc.):

_____

_____

_____

_____

_____

_____

_____

_____

_____

Notes:_____

_____

_____

_____

_____

_____

_____

_____

_____

_____

_____

_____

_____

_____

_____

_____

_____

_____

_____

_____

_____

_____

_____

_____

_____

_____

_____

_____

Nothing left to say? Use this page to paste in your favorite photos!

Location:_____,_____ Date of Trip:_____

The weather / temperature was:_____

Campground name:_____

Phone number:_____ Reservations needed by:_____

Site #:_____ Ideal Site #:_____ for possible return

Comments:_____

_____

The campground offered:_____

_____

Who I camped with:_____

_____

People I met:_____

_____

Places I visited:_____

_____

What I enjoyed most:_____

_____

Most memorable event:_____

_____

_____

Places to remember for the next time (restaurants, special attractions, entertainment, etc.):

_____

_____

_____

_____

_____

_____

_____

_____

_____

Notes:

Nothing left to say? Use this page to paste in your favorite photos!

Location:_____,_____ Date of Trip:_____

The weather / temperature was:_____

Campground name:_____

Phone number:_____ Reservations needed by:_____

Site #:_____ Ideal Site #:_____ for possible return

Comments:_____

_____

The campground offered:_____

_____

Who I camped with:_____

_____

People I met:_____

_____

Places I visited:_____

_____

What I enjoyed most:_____

_____

Most memorable event:_____

_____

_____

Places to remember for the next time (restaurants, special attractions, entertainment, etc.):

_____

_____

_____

_____

_____

_____

_____

_____

_____

Notes:

Nothing left to say? Use this page to paste in your favorite photos!

Location:_____ Date of Trip:_____

The weather / temperature was:_____

Campground name:_____

Phone number:_____ Reservations needed by:_____

Site #:_____ Ideal Site #:_____ for possible return

Comments:_____

_____

The campground offered:_____

_____

Who I camped with:_____

_____

People I met:_____

_____

Places I visited:_____

_____

What I enjoyed most:_____

_____

Most memorable event:_____

_____

_____

Places to remember for the next time (restaurants, special attractions, entertainment, etc.):

_____

_____

_____

_____

_____

_____

_____

_____

_____

Notes:

Nothing left to say? Use this page to paste in your favorite photos!

Location:_____, _____ Date of Trip:_____

The weather / temperature was:_____

Campground name:_____

Phone number:_____ Reservations needed by:_____

Site #:_____ Ideal Site #:_____ for possible return

Comments:_____

_____

The campground offered:_____

_____

Who I camped with:_____

_____

People I met:_____

_____

Places I visited:_____

_____

What I enjoyed most:_____

_____

Most memorable event:_____

_____

_____

Places to remember for the next time (restaurants, special attractions, entertainment, etc.):

_____

_____

_____

_____

_____

_____

_____

_____

_____

Notes:

Nothing left to say? Use this page to paste in your favorite photos!

Location:_____ Date of Trip:_____

The weather / temperature was:_____

Campground name:_____

Phone number:_____ Reservations needed by:_____

Site #:_____ Ideal Site #:_____ for possible return

Comments:_____

_____

The campground offered:_____

_____

Who I camped with:_____

_____

People I met:_____

_____

Places I visited:_____

_____

What I enjoyed most:_____

_____

Most memorable event:_____

_____

_____

Places to remember for the next time (restaurants, special attractions, entertainment, etc.):

_____

_____

_____

_____

_____

_____

_____

_____

_____

_____

Notes:

Nothing left to say? Use this page to paste in your favorite photos!

Location:_____,_____ Date of Trip:_____

The weather / temperature was:_____

Campground name:_____

Phone number:_____ Reservations needed by:_____

Site #:_____ Ideal Site #:_____ for possible return

Comments:_____

_____

The campground offered:_____

_____

Who I camped with:_____

_____

People I met:_____

_____

Places I visited:_____

_____

What I enjoyed most:_____

_____

Most memorable event:_____

_____

_____

Places to remember for the next time (restaurants, special attractions, entertainment, etc.):

_____

_____

_____

_____

_____

_____

_____

_____

_____

Notes:

Nothing left to say? Use this page to paste in your favorite photos!

Location:_____ Date of Trip:_____

The weather / temperature was:_____

Campground name:_____

Phone number:_____ Reservations needed by:_____

Site #:_____ Ideal Site #:_____ for possible return

Comments:_____

_____

The campground offered:_____

_____

Who I camped with:_____

_____

People I met:_____

_____

Places I visited:_____

_____

What I enjoyed most:_____

_____

Most memorable event:_____

_____

_____

Places to remember for the next time (restaurants, special attractions, entertainment, etc.):

_____

_____

_____

_____

_____

_____

_____

_____

_____

Notes:

Nothing left to say? Use this page to paste in your favorite photos!

Location:_____ Date of Trip:_____

The weather / temperature was:_____

Campground name:_____

Phone number:_____ Reservations needed by:_____

Site #:_____ Ideal Site #:_____ for possible return

Comments:_____
_____

The campground offered:_____
_____

Who I camped with:_____
_____

People I met:_____
_____

Places I visited:_____
_____

What I enjoyed most:_____
_____

Most memorable event:_____
_____
_____

Places to remember for the next time (restaurants, special attractions, entertainment, etc.):
_____
_____
_____
_____
_____
_____
_____
_____
_____

Notes:_____

_____

_____

_____

_____

_____

_____

_____

_____

_____

_____

_____

_____

_____

_____

_____

_____

_____

_____

_____

_____

_____

_____

_____

Nothing left to say? Use this page to paste in your favorite photos!

Location:_____ Date of Trip:_____

The weather / temperature was:_____

Campground name:_____

Phone number:_____ Reservations needed by:_____

Site #:_____ Ideal Site #:_____ for possible return

Comments:_____

_____

The campground offered:_____

_____

Who I camped with:_____

_____

People I met:_____

_____

Places I visited:_____

_____

What I enjoyed most:_____

_____

Most memorable event:_____

_____

_____

Places to remember for the next time (restaurants, special attractions, entertainment, etc.):

_____

_____

_____

_____

_____

_____

_____

_____

_____

_____

_____

Notes:_____

_____

_____

_____

_____

_____

_____

_____

_____

_____

_____

_____

_____

_____

_____

_____

_____

_____

_____

_____

_____

_____

_____

_____

_____

_____

_____

_____

_____

_____

_____

_____

_____

_____

*Nothing left to say? Use this page to paste in your favorite photos!*

Location:_____ Date of Trip:_____

The weather / temperature was:_____

Campground name:_____

Phone number:_____ Reservations needed by:_____

Site #:_____ Ideal Site #:_____ for possible return

Comments:_____

_____

The campground offered:_____

_____

Who I camped with:_____

_____

People I met:_____

_____

Places I visited:_____

_____

What I enjoyed most:_____

_____

Most memorable event:_____

_____

_____

Places to remember for the next time (restaurants, special attractions, entertainment, etc.):

_____

_____

_____

_____

_____

_____

_____

_____

_____

_____

Notes:

Nothing left to say? Use this page to paste in your favorite photos!

Location:_____ Date of Trip:_____

The weather / temperature was:_____

Campground name:_____

Phone number:_____ Reservations needed by:_____

Site #:_____ Ideal Site #:_____ for possible return

Comments:_____

_____

The campground offered:_____

_____

Who I camped with:_____

_____

People I met:_____

_____

Places I visited:_____

_____

What I enjoyed most:_____

_____

Most memorable event:_____

_____

_____

Places to remember for the next time (restaurants, special attractions, entertainment, etc.):

_____

_____

_____

_____

_____

_____

_____

_____

Notes:

Nothing left to say? Use this page to paste in your favorite photos!

Location:_____,_____ Date of Trip:_____

The weather / temperature was:_____

Campground name:_____

Phone number:_____ Reservations needed by:_____

Site #:_____ Ideal Site #:_____ for possible return

Comments:_____

_____

The campground offered:_____

_____

Who I camped with:_____

_____

People I met:_____

_____

Places I visited:_____

_____

What I enjoyed most:_____

_____

Most memorable event:_____

_____

_____

Places to remember for the next time (restaurants, special attractions, entertainment, etc.):

_____

_____

_____

_____

_____

_____

_____

_____

_____

Notes:

Nothing left to say? Use this page to paste in your favorite photos!

Location:_____ Date of Trip:_____

The weather / temperature was:_____

Campground name:_____

Phone number:_____ Reservations needed by:_____

Site #:_____ Ideal Site #:_____ for possible return

Comments:_____

_____

The campground offered:_____

_____

Who I camped with:_____

_____

People I met:_____

_____

Places I visited:_____

_____

What I enjoyed most:_____

_____

Most memorable event:_____

_____

_____

Places to remember for the next time (restaurants, special attractions, entertainment, etc.):

_____

_____

_____

_____

_____

_____

_____

_____

_____

_____

Notes:

Nothing left to say? Use this page to paste in your favorite photos!

Location:_____ Date of Trip:_____

The weather / temperature was:_____

Campground name:_____

Phone number:_____ Reservations needed by:_____

Site #:_____ Ideal Site #:_____ for possible return

Comments:_____

_____

The campground offered:_____

_____

Who I camped with:_____

_____

People I met:_____

_____

Places I visited:_____

_____

What I enjoyed most:_____

_____

Most memorable event:_____

_____

_____

Places to remember for the next time (restaurants, special attractions, entertainment, etc.):

_____

_____

_____

_____

_____

_____

_____

_____

_____

_____

Notes:

Nothing left to say? Use this page to paste in your favorite photos!

Location:_____,_____ Date of Trip:_____

The weather / temperature was:_____

Campground name:_____

Phone number:_____,_____ Reservations needed by:_____

Site #:_____ Ideal Site #:_____ for possible return

Comments:_____

_____

The campground offered:_____

_____

Who I camped with:_____

_____

People I met:_____

_____

Places I visited:_____

_____

What I enjoyed most:_____

_____

Most memorable event:_____

_____

Places to remember for the next time (restaurants, special attractions, entertainment, etc.):

_____

_____

_____

_____

_____

_____

_____

_____

Notes:

Nothing left to say? Use this page to paste in your favorite photos!

Location:_____,_____ Date of Trip:_____

The weather / temperature was:_____

Campground name:_____

Phone number:_____,_____ Reservations needed by:_____

Site #:_____ Ideal Site #:_____ for possible return

Comments:_____

_____

The campground offered:_____

_____

Who I camped with:_____

_____

People I met:_____

_____

Places I visited:_____

_____

What I enjoyed most:_____

_____

Most memorable event:_____

_____

_____

Places to remember for the next time (restaurants, special attractions, entertainment, etc.):

_____

_____

_____

_____

_____

_____

_____

_____

_____

Notes:

Nothing left to say? Use this page to paste in your favorite photos!

Location:_____ Date of Trip:_____

The weather / temperature was:_____

Campground name:_____

Phone number:_____ Reservations needed by:_____

Site #:_____ Ideal Site #:_____ for possible return

Comments:_____

_____

The campground offered:_____

_____

Who I camped with:_____

_____

People I met:_____

_____

Places I visited:_____

_____

What I enjoyed most:_____

_____

Most memorable event:_____

_____

_____

Places to remember for the next time (restaurants, special attractions, entertainment, etc.):

_____

_____

_____

_____

_____

_____

_____

_____

_____

Notes:

Nothing left to say? Use this page to paste in your favorite photos!

Location:_____ Date of Trip:_____

The weather / temperature was:_____

Campground name:_____

Phone number:_____ Reservations needed by:_____

Site #:_____ Ideal Site #:_____ for possible return

Comments:_____

_____

The campground offered:_____

_____

Who I camped with:_____

_____

People I met:_____

_____

Places I visited:_____

_____

What I enjoyed most:_____

_____

Most memorable event:_____

_____

_____

Places to remember for the next time (restaurants, special attractions, entertainment, etc.):

_____

_____

_____

_____

_____

_____

_____

_____

_____

_____

Notes:

Nothing left to say? Use this page to paste in your favorite photos!

Location:_____,_____ Date of Trip:_____

The weather / temperature was:_____

Campground name:_____

Phone number:_____,_____ Reservations needed by:_____

Site #:_____ Ideal Site #:_____ for possible return

Comments:_____

_____

The campground offered:_____

_____

Who I camped with:_____

_____

People I met:_____

_____

Places I visited:_____

_____

What I enjoyed most:_____

_____

Most memorable event:_____

_____

_____

Places to remember for the next time (restaurants, special attractions, entertainment, etc.):

_____

_____

_____

_____

_____

_____

_____

_____

_____

Notes:

Nothing left to say? Use this page to paste in your favorite photos!

Location:_____ Date of Trip:_____

The weather / temperature was:_____

Campground name:_____

Phone number:_____ Reservations needed by:_____

Site #:_____ Ideal Site #:_____ for possible return

Comments:_____

_____

The campground offered:_____

_____

Who I camped with:_____

_____

People I met:_____

_____

Places I visited:_____

_____

What I enjoyed most:_____

_____

Most memorable event:_____

_____

_____

Places to remember for the next time (restaurants, special attractions, entertainment, etc.):

_____

_____

_____

_____

_____

_____

_____

_____

_____

_____

Notes:

Nothing left to say? Use this page to paste in your favorite photos!

Location:_____ Date of Trip:_____

The weather / temperature was:_____

Campground name:_____

Phone number:_____ Reservations needed by:_____

Site #:_____ Ideal Site #:_____ for possible return

Comments:_____

_____

The campground offered:_____

_____

Who I camped with:_____

_____

People I met:_____

_____

Places I visited:_____

_____

What I enjoyed most:_____

_____

Most memorable event:_____

_____

_____

Places to remember for the next time (restaurants, special attractions, entertainment, etc.):

_____

_____

_____

_____

_____

_____

_____

_____

_____

Notes:_____

_____

_____

_____

_____

_____

_____

_____

_____

_____

_____

_____

_____

_____

_____

_____

_____

_____

_____

_____

_____

_____

_____

_____

_____

_____

_____

_____

_____

_____

_____

_____

Nothing left to say? Use this page to paste in your favorite photos!

Location:_____,_____ Date of Trip:_____

The weather / temperature was:_____

Campground name:_____,_____

Phone number:_____,_____ Reservations needed by:_____

Site #:_____ Ideal Site #:_____ for possible return

Comments:_____

_____

The campground offered:_____

_____

Who I camped with:_____

_____

People I met:_____

_____

Places I visited:_____

_____

What I enjoyed most:_____

_____

Most memorable event:_____

_____

_____

Places to remember for the next time (restaurants, special attractions, entertainment, etc.):

_____

_____

_____

_____

_____

_____

_____

_____

_____

_____

Notes:

Nothing left to say? Use this page to paste in your favorite photos!

Location:_____ Date of Trip:_____

The weather / temperature was:_____

Campground name:_____

Phone number:_____ Reservations needed by:_____

Site #:_____ Ideal Site #:_____ for possible return

Comments:_____

_____

The campground offered:_____

_____

Who I camped with:_____

_____

People I met:_____

_____

Places I visited:_____

_____

What I enjoyed most:_____

_____

Most memorable event:_____

_____

_____

Places to remember for the next time (restaurants, special attractions, entertainment, etc.):

_____

_____

_____

_____

_____

_____

_____

_____

_____

_____

Notes:_____

_____

_____

_____

_____

_____

_____

_____

_____

_____

_____

_____

_____

_____

_____

_____

_____

_____

_____

_____

_____

_____

_____

_____

_____

_____

_____

_____

_____

_____

_____

Nothing left to say? Use this page to paste in your favorite photos!

Location:_____ Date of Trip:_____

The weather / temperature was:_____

Campground name:_____

Phone number:_____ Reservations needed by:_____

Site #:_____ Ideal Site #:_____ for possible return

Comments:_____

_____

The campground offered:_____

_____

Who I camped with:_____

_____

People I met:_____

_____

Places I visited:_____

_____

What I enjoyed most:_____

_____

Most memorable event:_____

_____

_____

Places to remember for the next time (restaurants, special attractions, entertainment, etc.):

_____

_____

_____

_____

_____

_____

_____

_____

Notes:

Nothing left to say? Use this page to paste in your favorite photos!

Location:_____ Date of Trip:_____

The weather / temperature was:_____

Campground name:_____

Phone number:_____ Reservations needed by:_____

Site #:_____ Ideal Site #:_____ for possible return

Comments:_____

_____

The campground offered:_____

_____

Who I camped with:_____

_____

People I met:_____

_____

Places I visited:_____

_____

What I enjoyed most:_____

_____

Most memorable event:_____

_____

_____

Places to remember for the next time (restaurants, special attractions, entertainment, etc.):

_____

_____

_____

_____

_____

_____

_____

_____

_____

_____

Notes:

Nothing left to say? Use this page to paste in your favorite photos!

Location:_____ Date of Trip:_____

The weather / temperature was:_____

Campground name:_____

Phone number:_____ Reservations needed by:_____

Site #:_____ Ideal Site #:_____ for possible return

Comments:_____

_____

The campground offered:_____

_____

Who I camped with:_____

_____

People I met:_____

_____

Places I visited:_____

_____

What I enjoyed most:_____

_____

Most memorable event:_____

_____

_____

Places to remember for the next time (restaurants, special attractions, entertainment, etc.):

_____

_____

_____

_____

_____

_____

_____

_____

_____

Notes:_____

_____

_____

_____

_____

_____

_____

_____

_____

_____

_____

_____

_____

_____

_____

_____

_____

_____

_____

_____

_____

_____

_____

_____

_____

_____

_____

_____

_____

_____

Nothing left to say? Use this page to paste in your favorite photos!

Location:_____ Date of Trip:_____

The weather / temperature was:_____

Campground name:_____

Phone number:_____ Reservations needed by:_____

Site #:_____ Ideal Site #:_____ for possible return

Comments:_____

_____

The campground offered:_____

_____

Who I camped with:_____

_____

People I met:_____

_____

Places I visited:_____

_____

What I enjoyed most:_____

_____

Most memorable event:_____

_____

_____

Places to remember for the next time (restaurants, special attractions, entertainment, etc.):

_____

_____

_____

_____

_____

_____

_____

_____

_____

Notes:

Nothing left to say? Use this page to paste in your favorite photos!

Location:_____,_____ Date of Trip:_____

The weather / temperature was:_____

Campground name:_____

Phone number:_____,_____ Reservations needed by:_____

Site #:_____ Ideal Site #:_____ for possible return

Comments:_____

_____

The campground offered:_____

_____

Who I camped with:_____

_____

People I met:_____

_____

Places I visited:_____

_____

What I enjoyed most:_____

_____

Most memorable event:_____

_____

_____

Places to remember for the next time (restaurants, special attractions, entertainment, etc.):

_____

_____

_____

_____

_____

_____

_____

_____

_____

_____

Notes:

Nothing left to say? Use this page to paste in your favorite photos!

Location:_____ Date of Trip:_____

The weather / temperature was:_____

Campground name:_____

Phone number:_____ Reservations needed by:_____

Site #:_____ Ideal Site #:_____ for possible return

Comments:_____

_____

The campground offered:_____

_____

Who I camped with:_____

_____

People I met:_____

_____

Places I visited:_____

_____

What I enjoyed most:_____

_____

Most memorable event:_____

_____

_____

Places to remember for the next time (restaurants, special attractions, entertainment, etc.):

_____

_____

_____

_____

_____

_____

_____

_____

_____

Notes:

Nothing left to say? Use this page to paste in your favorite photos!

Location:_____ Date of Trip:_____

The weather / temperature was:_____

Campground name:_____

Phone number:_____ Reservations needed by:_____

Site #:_____ Ideal Site #:_____ for possible return

Comments:_____

_____

The campground offered:_____

_____

Who I camped with:_____

_____

People I met:_____

_____

Places I visited:_____

_____

What I enjoyed most:_____

_____

Most memorable event:_____

_____

_____

Places to remember for the next time (restaurants, special attractions, entertainment, etc.):

_____

_____

_____

_____

_____

_____

_____

_____

_____

Notes:

Nothing left to say? Use this page to paste in your favorite photos!

Location:_____ Date of Trip:_____

The weather / temperature was:_____

Campground name:_____

Phone number:_____ Reservations needed by:_____

Site #:_____ Ideal Site #:_____ for possible return

Comments:_____

_____

The campground offered:_____

_____

Who I camped with:_____

_____

People I met:_____

_____

Places I visited:_____

_____

What I enjoyed most:_____

_____

Most memorable event:_____

_____

_____

Places to remember for the next time (restaurants, special attractions, entertainment, etc.):

_____

_____

_____

_____

_____

_____

_____

_____

Notes:

Nothing left to say? Use this page to paste in your favorite photos!

Location:_____, _____ Date of Trip:_____

The weather / temperature was:_____

Campground name:_____

Phone number:_____ Reservations needed by:_____

Site #:_____ Ideal Site #:_____ for possible return

Comments:_____

_____

The campground offered:_____

_____

Who I camped with:_____

_____

People I met:_____

_____

Places I visited:_____

_____

What I enjoyed most:_____

_____

Most memorable event:_____

_____

_____

Places to remember for the next time (restaurants, special attractions, entertainment, etc.):

_____

_____

_____

_____

_____

_____

_____

_____

_____

Notes:

Nothing left to say? Use this page to paste in your favorite photos!

Location:_____ Date of Trip:_____

The weather / temperature was:_____

Campground name:_____

Phone number:_____ Reservations needed by:_____

Site #:_____ Ideal Site #:_____ for possible return

Comments:_____

_____

The campground offered:_____

_____

Who I camped with:_____

_____

People I met:_____

_____

Places I visited:_____

_____

What I enjoyed most:_____

_____

Most memorable event:_____

_____

_____

Places to remember for the next time (restaurants, special attractions, entertainment, etc.):

_____

_____

_____

_____

_____

_____

_____

_____

Notes:_____

_____

_____

_____

_____

_____

_____

_____

_____

_____

_____

_____

_____

_____

_____

_____

_____

_____

_____

_____

_____

_____

_____

_____

_____

_____

_____

_____

_____

_____

Nothing left to say? Use this page to paste in your favorite photos!

Location:_____ Date of Trip:_____

The weather / temperature was:_____

Campground name:_____

Phone number:_____ Reservations needed by:_____

Site #:_____ Ideal Site #:_____ for possible return

Comments:_____

_____

The campground offered:_____

_____

Who I camped with:_____

_____

People I met:_____

_____

Places I visited:_____

_____

What I enjoyed most:_____

_____

Most memorable event:_____

_____

_____

Places to remember for the next time (restaurants, special attractions, entertainment, etc.):

_____

_____

_____

_____

_____

_____

_____

_____

Notes:

Nothing left to say? Use this page to paste in your favorite photos!

Location:_____ Date of Trip:_____

The weather / temperature was:_____

Campground name:_____

Phone number:_____ Reservations needed by:_____

Site #:_____ Ideal Site #:_____ for possible return

Comments:_____

_____

The campground offered:_____

_____

Who I camped with:_____

_____

People I met:_____

_____

Places I visited:_____

_____

What I enjoyed most:_____

_____

Most memorable event:_____

_____

_____

Places to remember for the next time (restaurants, special attractions, entertainment, etc.):

_____

_____

_____

_____

_____

_____

_____

_____

_____

Notes:

Nothing left to say? Use this page to paste in your favorite photos!

Location:_____ Date of Trip:_____

The weather / temperature was:_____

Campground name:_____

Phone number:_____ Reservations needed by:_____

Site #:_____ Ideal Site #:_____ for possible return

Comments:_____

_____

The campground offered:_____

_____

Who I camped with:_____

_____

People I met:_____

_____

Places I visited:_____

_____

What I enjoyed most:_____

_____

Most memorable event:_____

_____

_____

Places to remember for the next time (restaurants, special attractions, entertainment, etc.):

_____

_____

_____

_____

_____

_____

_____

_____

_____

Notes:

Nothing left to say? Use this page to paste in your favorite photos!

www.journalsunlimited.com

Location:_____ Date of Trip:_____

The weather / temperature was:_____

Campground name:_____

Phone number:_____ Reservations needed by:_____

Site #:_____ Ideal Site #:_____ for possible return

Comments:_____

_____

The campground offered:_____

_____

Who I camped with:_____

_____

People I met:_____

_____

Places I visited:_____

_____

What I enjoyed most:_____

_____

Most memorable event:_____

_____

_____

Places to remember for the next time (restaurants, special attractions, entertainment, etc.):

_____

_____

_____

_____

_____

_____

_____

_____

_____

Notes:_____

_____

_____

_____

_____

_____

_____

_____

_____

_____

_____

_____

_____

_____

_____

_____

_____

_____

_____

_____

_____

_____

_____

_____

_____

_____

_____

_____

_____

_____

_____

Nothing left to say? Use this page to paste in your favorite photos!

Location:_____ Date of Trip:_____

The weather / temperature was:_____

Campground name:_____

Phone number:_____ Reservations needed by:_____

Site #:_____ Ideal Site #:_____ for possible return

Comments:_____

_____

The campground offered:_____

_____

Who I camped with:_____

_____

People I met:_____

_____

Places I visited:_____

_____

What I enjoyed most:_____

_____

Most memorable event:_____

_____

_____

Places to remember for the next time (restaurants, special attractions, entertainment, etc.):

_____

_____

_____

_____

_____

_____

_____

_____

_____

Notes:

Nothing left to say? Use this page to paste in your favorite photos!

Location:_____ Date of Trip:_____

The weather / temperature was:_____

Campground name:_____

Phone number:_____ Reservations needed by:_____

Site #:_____ Ideal Site #:_____ for possible return

Comments:_____

_____

The campground offered:_____

_____

Who I camped with:_____

_____

People I met:_____

_____

Places I visited:_____

_____

What I enjoyed most:_____

_____

Most memorable event:_____

_____

_____

Places to remember for the next time (restaurants, special attractions, entertainment, etc.):

_____

_____

_____

_____

_____

_____

_____

_____

_____

Notes:_____

_____

_____

_____

_____

_____

_____

_____

_____

_____

_____

_____

_____

_____

_____

_____

_____

_____

_____

_____

_____

_____

_____

_____

_____

_____

_____

_____

Nothing left to say? Use this page to paste in your favorite photos!

Location:_____,_____ Date of Trip:_____

The weather / temperature was:_____

Campground name:_____

Phone number:_____,_____ Reservations needed by:_____

Site #:_____ Ideal Site #:_____ for possible return

Comments:_____

_____

The campground offered:_____

_____

Who I camped with:_____

_____

People I met:_____

_____

Places I visited:_____

_____

What I enjoyed most:_____

_____

Most memorable event:_____

_____

_____

Places to remember for the next time (restaurants, special attractions, entertainment, etc.):

_____

_____

_____

_____

_____

_____

_____

_____

Notes:

Nothing left to say? Use this page to paste in your favorite photos!

Location:_____ Date of Trip:_____

The weather / temperature was:_____

Campground name:_____

Phone number:_____ Reservations needed by:_____

Site #:_____ Ideal Site #:_____ for possible return

Comments:_____
_____

The campground offered:_____
_____

Who I camped with:_____
_____

People I met:_____
_____

Places I visited:_____
_____

What I enjoyed most:_____
_____

Most memorable event:_____
_____
_____

Places to remember for the next time (restaurants, special attractions, entertainment, etc.):
_____
_____
_____
_____
_____
_____
_____
_____

Notes:

Nothing left to say? Use this page to paste in your favorite photos!

Location:_____ Date of Trip:_____

The weather / temperature was:_____

Campground name:_____

Phone number:_____ Reservations needed by:_____

Site #:_____ Ideal Site #:_____ for possible return

Comments:_____

_____

The campground offered:_____

_____

Who I camped with:_____

_____

People I met:_____

_____

Places I visited:_____

_____

What I enjoyed most:_____

_____

Most memorable event:_____

_____

_____

Places to remember for the next time (restaurants, special attractions, entertainment, etc.):

_____

_____

_____

_____

_____

_____

_____

_____

_____

Notes: _____

_____

_____

_____

_____

_____

_____

_____

_____

_____

_____

_____

_____

_____

_____

_____

_____

_____

_____

_____

_____

_____

_____

_____

_____

_____

_____

_____

_____

_____

_____

_____

_____

Nothing left to say? Use this page to paste in your favorite photos!

Location:_____ Date of Trip:_____

The weather / temperature was:_____

Campground name:_____

Phone number:_____ Reservations needed by:_____

Site #:_____ Ideal Site #:_____ for possible return

Comments:_____

_____

The campground offered:_____

_____

Who I camped with:_____

_____

People I met:_____

_____

Places I visited:_____

_____

What I enjoyed most:_____

_____

Most memorable event:_____

_____

_____

Places to remember for the next time (restaurants, special attractions, entertainment, etc.):

_____

_____

_____

_____

_____

_____

_____

_____

Notes:

Nothing left to say? Use this page to paste in your favorite photos!